Each manga title has the unique style and voice of its creator. All the manga are presented in the right-to-left format just as they are in Japan, which allows the panels to be displayed as the creator originally intended, and adds authenticity and fun to the reader's experience.

So brace yourself for an amazing adventure with SHONEN JUMP. Here's a taste of the most intense action, craziest nail-biting cliffhangers and coolest characters around. You're about to JUMP headfirst into the world of manga. Enjoy!

Be sure to flip the book over for a look at two more outstanding VIZ Media series:

Find out more about your favourite SHONEN JUMP and VIZ Media manga titles now at www.simonsays.co.uk.

VIZ Media products are distributed by Simon & Schuster in the U.K. For sales information, please contact:
Simon & Schuster UK
Africa House
64-78 Kingsway
London WC2B 6AH
UK
Email: enquiries @simonandschuster.co.uk

www.vizeurope.com

Contents

SHONEN JUMP / SHONEN JUMP ADVANCED
Sneak Peek
[2]

Printed in the U.K.

Published by VIZ Media, LLC
P.O. Box 77010
San Francisco, CA 94107

BUSOU RENKIN © 2003 by Nobuhiro Watsuki
All rights reserved.
First published in Japan in 2003 by SHUEISHA Inc., Tokyo.
English translation rights arranged by SHUEISHA Inc.

THE PRINCE OF TENNIS © 1999 by Takeshi Konomi
All rights reserved.
First published in Japan in 1999 by SHUEISHA Inc., Tokyo.
English translation rights arranged by SHUEISHA Inc.

D.GRAY-MAN © 2004 by Katsura Hoshino
All rights reserved.
First published in Japan in 2004 by SHUEISHA Inc., Tokyo.
English translation rights arranged by SHUEISHA Inc.

YU-GI-OH! © 1996 by Kazuki Takahashi
All rights reserved.
First published in Japan in 1996 by SHUEISHA Inc., Tokyo.
English translation rights arranged by SHUEISHA Inc.

The stories, characters and incidents mentioned in this publication are entirely fictional.

Project Manager/Carrie Shepherd
Design/Fawn Lau
Editor in Chief, Books/Alvin Lu
Editor in Chief, Magazines/Marc Weidenbaum
VP of Publishing Licensing/Rika Inouye
VP of Sales/Gonzalo Ferreyra
Sr. VP of Marketing/Liza Coppola
Publisher/Hyoe Narita

BUSO RENKIN
STORY AND ART BY NOBUHIRO WATSUKI
Translation & English Adaptation/Mayumi Kobayashi
Touch-up Art & Lettering/James Gaubatz
Design/Yukiko Whitley
Editors/Michelle Pangilinan & Urian Brown

THE PRINCE OF TENNIS
STORY AND ART BY TAKESHI KONOMI
English Adaptation/Gerard Jones
Translation/Joe Yamazaki
Touch-up Art & Lettering/Andy Ristaino
Design/Sean Lee
Editor/Urian Brown

D.GRAY-MAN
STORY AND ART BY KATSURA HOSHINO
Translation & English Adaptation/Mayumi Kobayashi
Touch-up Art & Lettering/Elizabeth Watasin
Design/Yukiko Whitley
Editor/Michelle Pangilinan

YU-GI-OH!: MILLENNIUM WORLD
STORY AND ART BY KAZUKI TAKAHASHI
Translation & English Adaptation/Anita Sengupta
Touch-up Art & Lettering/Kelle Han
Additional Touch-up/Josh Simpson
Design/Sean Lee
Editor/Jason Thompson

ratings.viz.com   ratings.viz.com   ratings.viz.com

**STORY AND ART BY
NOBUHIRO WATSUKI**

Buso Renkin is the story of teenager Kazuki Muto, who dies trying to save a girl who was being attacked by an eerie monster. The next morning, however, Kazuki is left wondering whether it was all a dream. Lo and behold, the girl, the monster, and his death are all real! The girl, Tokiko Tsumura, was actually trying to slay the homunculus (a beast that can take the form of humans, and whose main source of food is people), but Kazuki got in her way. To revive Kazuki, Tokiko replaces his heart with a "kakugane," an alchemic device that allows him to summon a lance with which to fight the monsters. It turns out that Tokiko is a member of the Alchemist Warriors, an organization sworn to protect the world from the diabolical creatures. Soon, Kazuki joins Tokiko in her quest to terminate the sinister being that creates and controls the homunculi.

CHAPTER 1: NEW LIFE
Nobuhiro Watsuki

IT'S THE BELL.

GO! OR DO YOU WANT MORE DEMERITS?

EH?!

RING

YOU'RE NOT ALLOWED TO LEAVE UNTIL YOU'RE DONE.

I DON'T CARE IF IT TAKES YOU ALL NIGHT.

...YOU...

FOUND...

RUSTLE RUSTLE

DON'T YOU THINK MITA'S BEEN ACTING STRANGE LATELY?

LUNCHTIME

WHAT DO YOU THINK?

YOU THINK? I'VE ALWAYS THOUGHT HE WAS THE HARDEST TEACHER TO DEAL WITH AT SCHOOL.

RUSTLE RUSTLE

HEY MAHIRO!

AH!

FOUND YOU GUYS!

I SEE. YEAH, HE'S NOT GOOD AT ROCK-PAPER-SCISSORS.

TAK TAK TAK

HUH? WHERE'S MY BROTHER?

HE WENT TO BUY US DRINKS.

GOT 'EM!

REALLY?

THE UNIFORM LOOKS GOOD ON YOU.

CONGRATULATIONS ON GETTING INTO OUR SCHOOL.

THANKS.

**STORY AND ART BY
TAKESHI KONOMI**

Ryoma Echizen just joined the Seishun Academy's tennis team, which is known for being one of the most competitive teams in Japan. Its members are incredibly talented, gifted and athletic. With rigorous and extremely intense practices, the upperclassmen of the team expect the very best from themselves and even more from the new members of the team. While most of the freshmen are on pins and needles hoping they won't get cut from the team, Ryoma Echizen is confident, cool and collected. Some might even say he's cocky, but at least he's got the skills to back up his attitude. With his virtually unreturnable "twist serve," Ryoma is sure to make the starting team.

Join Ryoma and the other first years, as they train hard, make friends and try to find a place for themselves on the team. Ryoma Echizen is the Prince of Tennis. He may be ready for the Seishun Academy tennis team, but are THEY ready for HIM?

THE PRINCE OF TENNIS © 1999 by Takeshi Konomi/SHUEISHA Inc.

GENIUS 1:

RYOMA ECHIZEN

OH! I HAVE TO GET OFF HERE TOO!!

SHE INVITED ME TO THE TENNIS TOURNAMENT WITH HER, BUT AT THIS RATE I'M GOING TO BE LATE...

GRANDMA ISN'T HERE...

TURN

ACK! H-HE'S LOOKING THIS WAY?!

HUH?! IT'S THAT BOY!

HEY... WHICH WAY ARE THE KAKINOKIZAKA TENNIS GROUNDS?

ONE-SET MATCH.

MY SERVE.

RETURN IT!!

THIS KID WON'T EVEN BLOCK THE SERVE...

BMM

TONG

**STORY AND ART BY
KATSURA HOSHINO**

Set in a fictional 19th-century England,

D.Gray-man is the story of Allen Walker, a 15-year-old boy who roams the earth in search of Innocence. Washed away to unknown parts of the world after the Great Flood, Innocence is the mysterious substance used to create weapons that obliterate demons known as *akuma*.

EXORCISTS...

THEY EXIST TO DESTROY THE OMINOUS EVILS THAT RISE FROM THE DARKNESS.

THOSE POSSESSED BY THE GODS...

THE 1st NIGHT: *Opening*

FLAP

FLAP

FLAP

UGH...

CAN'T
...

...BREATHE
...

IT CAN'T BE...

THE RUMOR WAS TRUE?

?!

GRAB

**STORY AND ART BY
KAZUKI TAKAHASHI**

The final saga of the *Yu-Gi-Oh!* epic! After many deadly duels, Yugi has collected the three Egyptian God Cards, the key to remembering his own past life as an Egyptian pharaoh. When the cards take Yugi's soul back in time, can he defeat the villains of the past and achieve his ultimate destiny?

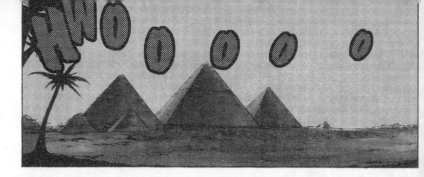

EGYPT • VALLEY OF THE KINGS • 1960

Duel 1: The Millennium Treasure

Duel 1: The Millennium Treasure

NOT EVEN THE ARCHAEOLOGISTS ...

NOT THE GRAVE ROBBERS ...

HOWEVER, RUMOR SAYS IN 3,000 YEARS, THAT *NOT ONE* PERSON HAS MADE IT TO THE DEPTHS OF *THAT* TOMB...

OVER 60 TOMBS HAVE BEEN DISCOVERED IN THIS VALLEY. MOST OF THEM HAVE BEEN RANSACKED ...

THE VALLEY OF THE KINGS...

THE GRAVEYARD OF THE PHARAOHS OF EGYPT'S NEW KINGDOM (1550–1070 B.C.). IT IS LOCATED IN A DEEP *WADI* (VALLEY) WEST OF THE NILE RIVER, NEAR LUXOR.

OR SO THEY SAY...

"*THE SHADOW GAMES* ..."

AT THE BEGINNING OF THIS CENTURY ONE OF THE BRITISH ROYAL ARCHAEOLOGICAL TEAM SAID THIS WITH HIS LAST BREATH...

VALLEY OF THE KINGS ○   ○ LUXOR

THE SHADOW GAMES ...

WE'LL LEAD YOU TO THE *OPENING* OF THE ROYAL TOMB...BUT AFTER THAT, *YOU* PUT *YOUR* NECK ON THE LINE TO LEAD US TO THE TREASURE!

WE'RE NOT FOOLS LIKE YOU WHO'D THROW OUR LIVES AWAY FOR A GAME...

JUST SO YOU KNOW ...

ONLY THE ONE WHO *WINS* THE GAMES CAN GET TO THE GOLDEN TREASURE HIDDEN BEYOND...

THIS GAME IS DESIGNED TO **TEST** THE WISDOM AND HUMILITY OF INTRUDERS!

JUST DO IT!!

WATCH YOUR STEP!

RM MMM MB

I CAN'T...

EEP!

...THE "OPENER OF THE WAY"!

THIS STATUE OVER THE NEXT DOOR SHOWS THE PHARAOH WITH THE BODY OF HORUS, THE FALCON GOD...

DASH

MUSHARA!

SSSSS UP

SH UK

AAGGHHH!

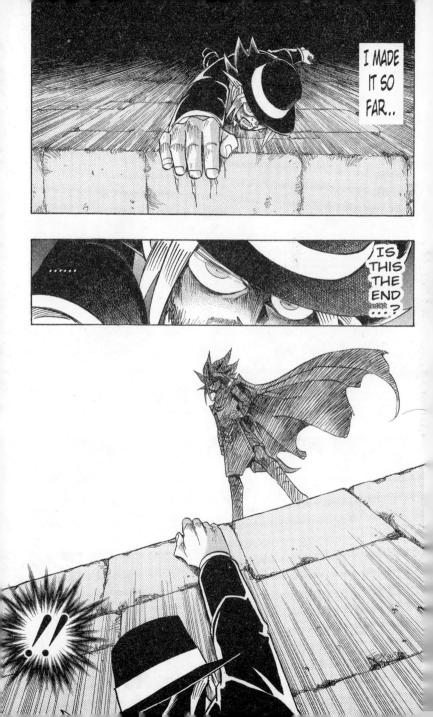

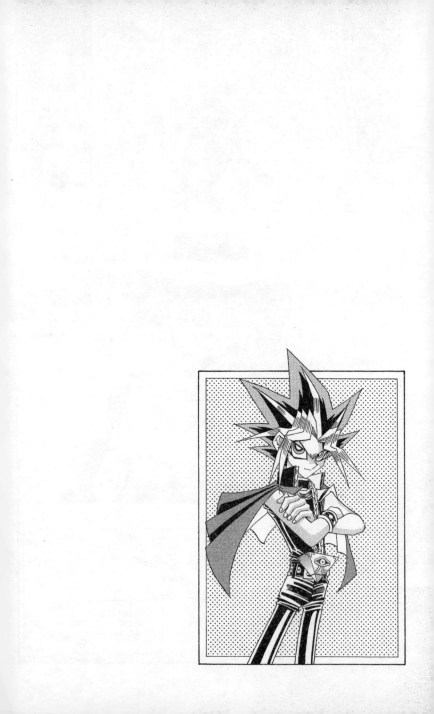

Duel 2:
A Sleepless Night

THE THREE GOD CARDS THAT THE OTHER ME FOUGHT HARD TO WIN IN BATTLE CITY...

THE GOD CARDS ARE IN THIS BOX.

THEY'RE A PIECE OF THE *PUZZLE* IN THE SEARCH FOR HIS MEMORIES...

Duel 2:
A Sleepless Night

FSSH

"THAT IS THE FATE OF THE CHOSEN ONE..."

...

WHY DID GRANDPA SAY THAT ...?

BUT NOW I FEEL SO RESTLESS IT ALMOST HURTS...

ANYWAY, WE'LL FIND OUT SOMETHING AT THE MUSEUM TOMORROW ...

MEMORIES ...

BAKURA SAID SOMETHING TO ME BEFORE ...

"TO AWAKEN THE PHARAOH'S MEMORIES IS THE DUTY OF THE ONE CHOSEN BY THE PUZZLE..."

WAIT!
There's more!

FLIP this book over for a sneak peek
of *HAYATE THE COMBAT BUTLER* and
MEGAMAN NT WARRIOR!

FLIP

139

Taking on the afterlife one soul at a time...

Manga series on sale now!

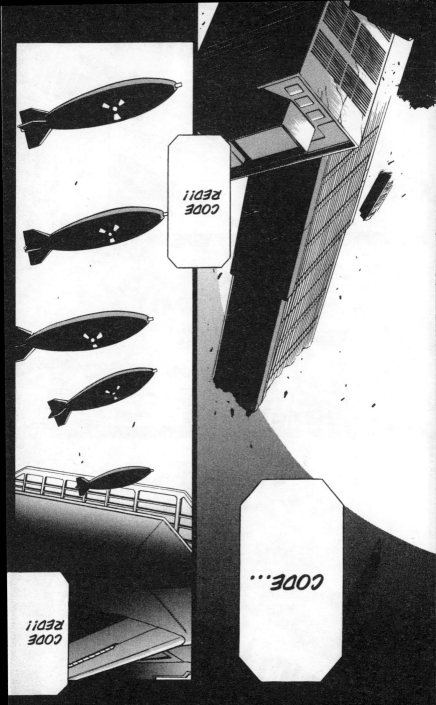

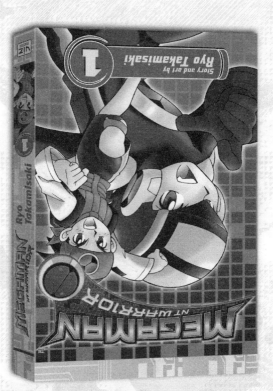

STORY AND ART BY RYO TAKAMISAKI

It's the year 200X and everyone in Den Tech City is plugged into the Net. But living in cyberspace isn't always fun and games. High-tech crimes and pesky viruses are always a big problem for the authorities. Thank goodness for MegaMan and his NetOperator, Lan Hikari. Together, they do their best to keep their hometown from being permanently deleted.

A DETECTIVE IN NEED OF A CLUE

CASE CLOSED™

With an innate talent for observation and intuition, Jimmy can solve mysteries that leave the most seasoned law enforcement officials baffled. But when a strange chemical transforms him from a high school teenager to a grade schooler who no one takes seriously, will this be one mystery this sleuth can't solve?

Start your graphic novel collection today!

www.viz.com
store.viz.com

RATED

T+ FOR OLDER TEEN

ratings.viz.com

Since the tender age of 9, Hayate Ayasaki has busted his behind at various part-time jobs to support his degenerate gambler parents. And how do they repay their son's selfless generosity? By selling his organs to the yakuza to cover their debts! But fate throws Hayate a bone...sort of.

STORY AND ART BY
KENJIRO HATA

Contents

Hayate the Combat Butler

STORY AND ART BY KENJIRO HATA

MEGAMAN NT WARRIOR

STORY AND ART BY RYO TAKAMISAKI

VIZ MEDIA
Sneak Peek
[2]

Published by VIZ Media, LLC
P.O. Box 77010
San Francisco, CA 94107

HAYATE THE COMBAT BUTLER © 2005 Kenjiro HATA/Shogakukan Inc. First published by Shogakukan Inc. in Japan as "Hayate no Gotoku."

MEGAMAN NT WARIOR © 2001 Ryo TAKAMISAKI/Shogakukan Inc. © CAPCOM Co., Ltd. ™and ® are trademarks of CAPCOM Co., Ltd. First published by Shogakukan Inc. in Japan as "Rokkuman Eguze"

The stories, characters and incidents mentioned in this publication are entirely fictional.

Project Manager/Carrie Shepherd
Design/Fawn Lau
Editor in Chief, Books/Alvin Lu
Editor in Chief, Magazines/Marc Weidenbaum
VP of Publishing Licensing/Rika Inouye
VP of Sales/Gonzalo Ferreyra
Sr. VP of Marketing/Liza Coppola
Publisher/Hyoe Narita

HAYATE THE COMBAT BUTLER
STORY AND ART BY KENJIRO HATA
English Adaptation/Mark Giambruno
Translation/Yuki Yoshioka & Cindy H. Yamauchi
Touch-up Art & Lettering/Freeman Wong
Design/Yukiko Whitley
Editor/Kit Fox

MEGAMAN NT WARRIOR
STORY AND ART BY RYO TAKAMISAKI
English Adaptation/Gary Leach
Translation/Koji Goto
Touch-up Art & Lettering/Gia Cam Luc
Design/Carolina Ugalde
Editor/Eric Searleman

RATED
A
FOR
ALL AGES
ratings.viz.com

RATED
T+
FOR OLDER TEEN
ratings.viz.com